# Teacher's Resource Masters
## Measurement and Data

Daily Common Core Review

Reteaching

Practice

Enrichment

Scott Foresman·Addison Wesl

# enVisionMATH
## Common C

**PEARSON**

Glenview, Illinois • Boston, Massachusetts • Chandler, Arizona • Upper Saddle River, New Je

**PEARSON**

ISBN-13: 978-0-328-68773-2
ISBN-10: 0-328-68773-1

3 4 5 6 7 8 9 10 V042 15 14 13 12 11

# Domain
# Measurement and Data

Each lesson has a Teacher Resource Master for Daily
Common Core Review, Reteaching, Practice and Enrichment.

## Topic 12 **Measurement**

## Topic 13 **Sorting, Classifying, Counting, and Categorizing Data**

Name _____

 1

Ⓐ 2 + 0 = 2      Ⓒ 2 + 2 = 4

Ⓑ 2 + 1 = 3      Ⓓ 3 + 1 = 4

---

 2

10          9          8          7

Ⓐ          Ⓑ          Ⓒ          Ⓓ

---

**Directions** Have children mark the best answer. ⭐ Which number sentence tells how many bees in all? ❷ Which number tells how many pinecones?

# Describing Objects by More Than One Attribute

 **1**

**2**

**3**

**Directions** Have children look at each object and circle the tools that they can use to tell about the attributes of the object.

# Describing Objects by More Than One Attribute

**★1**

**②2**

**③3**

**④4**

**Directions** Have children look at each object and circle the tools they could use to tell about the attributes of the object.

# What Will Fit?

**Directions** Have children look at the objects and draw a line to the basket if the objects will fit in the basket. Then have them mark an X on the objects that will **not** fit in the basket.

E 12·1

Name _____

 | 4 | 5 | 6 | | 8 |

(A) 9

(B) 7

(C) 6

(D) 0

---

2  ○ ○ ○ ⊗ ⊗

(A) $5 - 2 = 3$

(B) $5 - 3 = 2$

(C) $5 - 4 = 1$

(D) $5 - 5 = 0$

---

**Directions** Have children mark the best answer. ⭐ Which number is missing? ② Which subtraction sentence tells about the counters?

# Comparing by Length

**1**

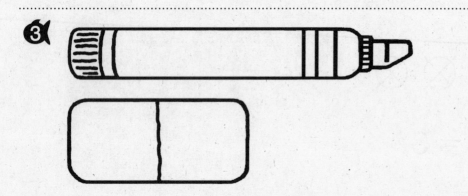

**2**

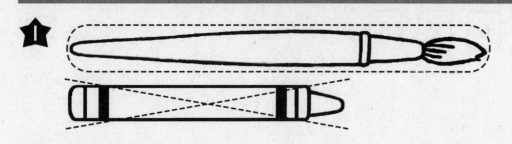

**3**

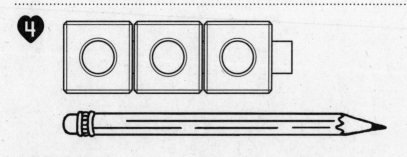

**4**

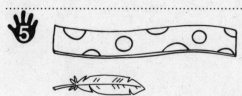

**5**

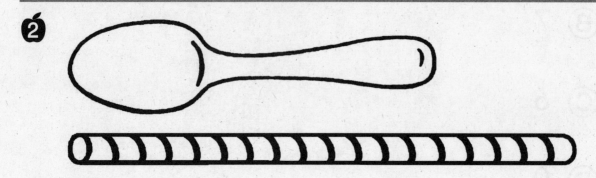

**Directions** Have children: **1** circle the longer object and mark an X on the shorter object; **2**–**3** circle the longer object; **4**–**5** mark an X on the shorter object.

# Comparing by Length

**1**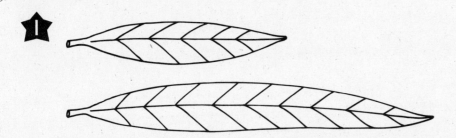

**2**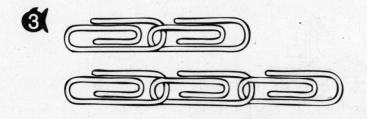

**3**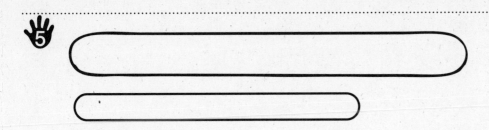

**4**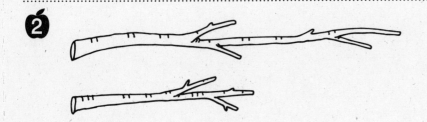

**5**

**Directions** Have children circle the longer object and mark an X on the shorter object. If the objects are the same length, underline both of them.

Name _____

# Longer or Shorter?

**1**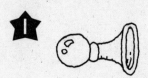

---

**2**

---

**Directions** Have children: ⭐ draw an object that is shorter or longer than the horn, and then color the object red if it is shorter or blue if it is longer; ❷ draw an object that is shorter or longer than the clown car, and then color the object yellow if it is shorter or purple if it is longer.

E 12·2

⭐

Ⓐ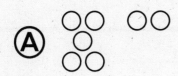

Ⓑ

Ⓒ

Ⓓ

❷

Ⓐ

Ⓑ

Ⓒ

Ⓓ

**Directions** Have children mark the best answer. ⭐ Which picture shows 7 counters? ❷ Which picture shows 2 fewer leaves than the group shown?

Name _____

# More Comparing Objects by Length

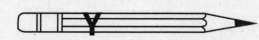  

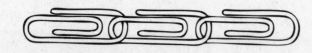

**Directions** Have children color the longest object red and the shortest object yellow.

Name _____

# More Comparing Objects by Length

**1**

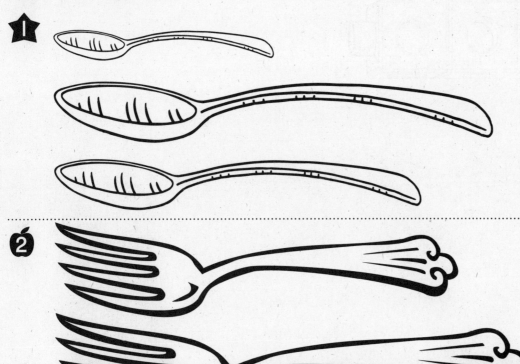

**2**

**3**

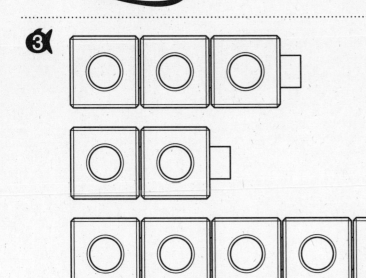

**Directions** Have children circle the longest object and mark an X on the shortest object.

Name _____

# What's My Size?

**1**

**2**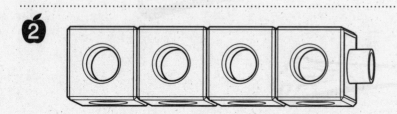

⭐  6 7 8

Ⓐ 0

Ⓑ 6

Ⓒ 7

Ⓓ 9

❷

Ⓐ

Ⓑ

Ⓒ

Ⓓ

---

**Directions** Have children mark the best answer. ⭐ Which number comes after 8? ❷ Which picture shows two less?

Name _____

# Problem Solving:
# Try, Check, and Revise

**1**

**2**

**3**

**4**

---

**Directions** *Jared is using paper strips for a project. He tries to order the paper strips from shortest to longest. How can we check his work?* Provide children with paper strips that measure 2 inches, 3 inches, 4 inches, and 5 inches. Have children compare and order the paper strips from shortest to longest and then write the numbers to show the correct order from shortest to longest (1–4).

Name _____

# Problem Solving:
# Try, Check, and Revise

_____
- - - - - - - - -
_____

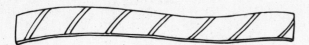

_____
- - - - - - - - -
_____

_____
- - - - - - - - -
_____

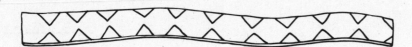

_____
- - - - - - - - -
_____

**Directions** *Olivia wants to compare pieces of ribbon to find the shortest and longest. How can we compare the pieces? How can we check and revise?* Have children compare and order the pieces of ribbon from shortest to longest, write the numbers to show the correct order from shortest to longest (1–4), and then discuss the process and results.

# How Long Am I?

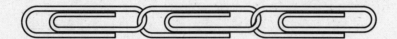

## Guess

_____

------------

_____

## Length

_____

------------

_____

**Directions** Have children choose an object in the classroom that is longer than a paper clip chain made with 3 paper clips. Have them draw the object, guess and write how many paper clips long they think the object is, and then measure with paper clips to write the length.

(A) ☆

(B) ☆ ☆

(C) ☆ ☆ ☆ ☆

(D) ☆ ☆ ☆ ☆ ☆

---

**2**

 MARKER

(A)

(B)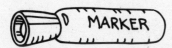

(C)

(D)

---

**Directions** Have children mark the best answer. 1 Which picture shows more than 4 stars? 2 Which object is longer than the marker?

# Comparing by Height

 **1**

**2**

**3**

 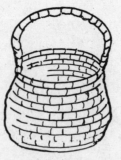

Name _____

# Comparing by Height

 **1**

 **2**

 **3**

**4**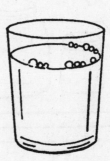

 **5**

**6**

**Directions** Have children circle the taller object and mark an X on the shorter object. If the objects are the same height, underline both of them.

Name _____

# Shorter or Taller?

**Directions** Have children look at each pair of objects, color the taller object in each pair green, and color the shorter object in each pair yellow. If the objects are the same height, color both objects blue.

⭐

_____

- - - - - - - - - - -

_____ more

....................................

🍎 | 8 | 10 | 7 | 9 |

_____    _____    _____    _____

- - - - - - -   - - - - - - -   - - - - - - -   - - - - - - -

_____    _____    _____    _____

**Directions** Have children: ⭐ draw lines to compare groups and write the number; 🍎 write the numbers in order.

D 12·6

Copyright © Pearson Education, Inc., or its affiliates. All Rights Reserved. **K**

# More Comparing Objects
# by Height

 **1**

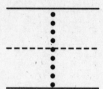        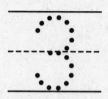

 **2**

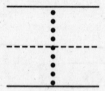        

**3**

    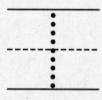    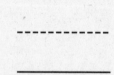

**Directions** Have children write the numbers 1, 2, and 3 to show the containers in order from shortest to tallest.

**R 12·6**

Name _____

# More Comparing Objects by Height

**1**

**2**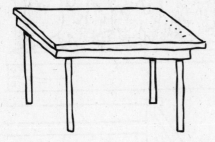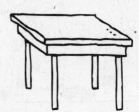

**3**

**4**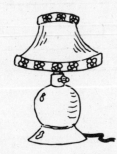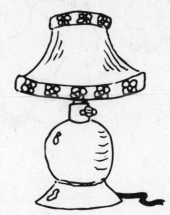

---

**Directions** Have children circle the tallest object and mark an X on the shortest object.

# Shortest and Tallest on the Farm

**Directions** Have children order the animals in each group by coloring the tallest animals red and the shortest animals yellow.

Name _____

Name _____

Name _____

Name _____

**1**

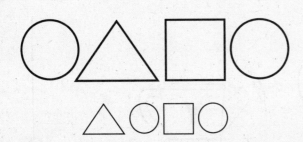

---

**2**

---

**Directions** Have children: **1** circle the row of shapes that is smaller; **2** color the fish that are bigger red and the fish that are smaller blue.

Name _____

# Comparing Capacities

**Directions** Have children color the watering can that holds more green and the watering can that holds less yellow. Then have them look at each of the other four pairs of containers, and color the one in each pair green that holds more; color yellow the container in each pair that holds less.

Name _____

# Comparing Capacities

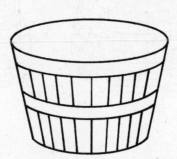

**Directions** Have children compare objects by drawing a line from the object on the left that holds less to the matching object on the right that holds more.

Name _____

# Holding Power

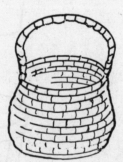

**Directions** Have children circle the containers that can hold the least. Then have children draw a container in each set that holds the most.

Ⓐ           Ⓒ

Ⓑ           Ⓓ

---

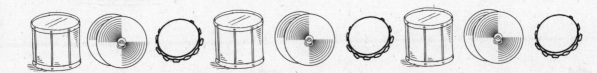

Ⓐ           Ⓒ

Ⓑ           Ⓓ

---

**Directions** Have children mark the best answer. ⭐ Which shape is third in line? ② If there were two less items in the line, what would the last item in line be?

Name _____

# Comparing by Weight

**1**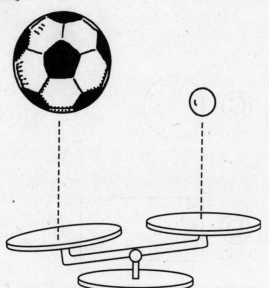

**2**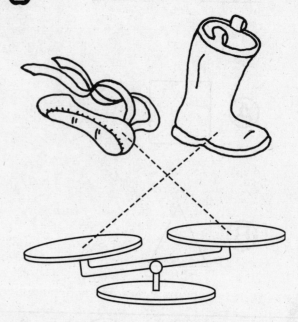

**3**

**4**

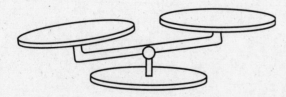

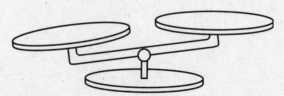

**Directions** Have children look at the objects and decide which object is heavier and which object is lighter. Then have them match the heavier object to the low side of the scale and match the lighter object to the high side of the scale.

Name _____

# Comparing by Weight

**1**

**2**

**3**

**4**

**5**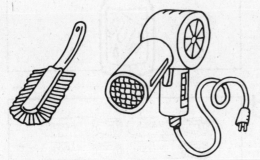

**6**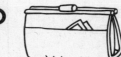

**Directions** Have children compare each pair of objects and then mark an X on the lighter object.

Name _____

# More? Less? Same?

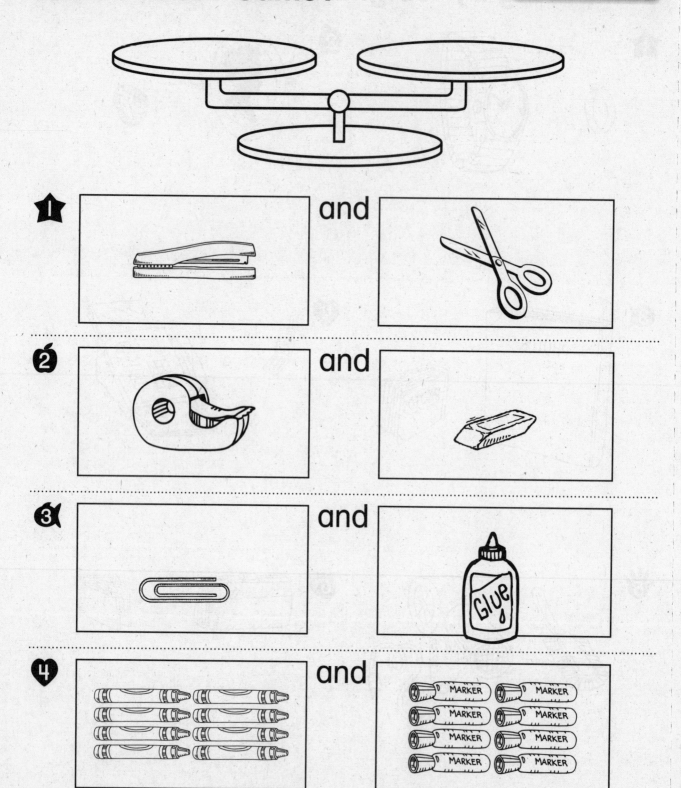

Name _____

 1

Ⓐ

Ⓑ

Ⓒ

Ⓓ

🍎 2

Ⓐ

Ⓑ

Ⓒ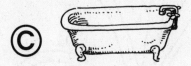

Ⓓ

⭐ 3

Ⓐ 6

Ⓑ 4

Ⓒ 3

Ⓓ 2

---

**Directions** Have children mark the best answer. ⭐ Which picture shows the container that holds more than the one shown? 🍎 Which is the heaviest object? ⭐ Which number tells how many marbles are left?

Name _____

# Same and Different

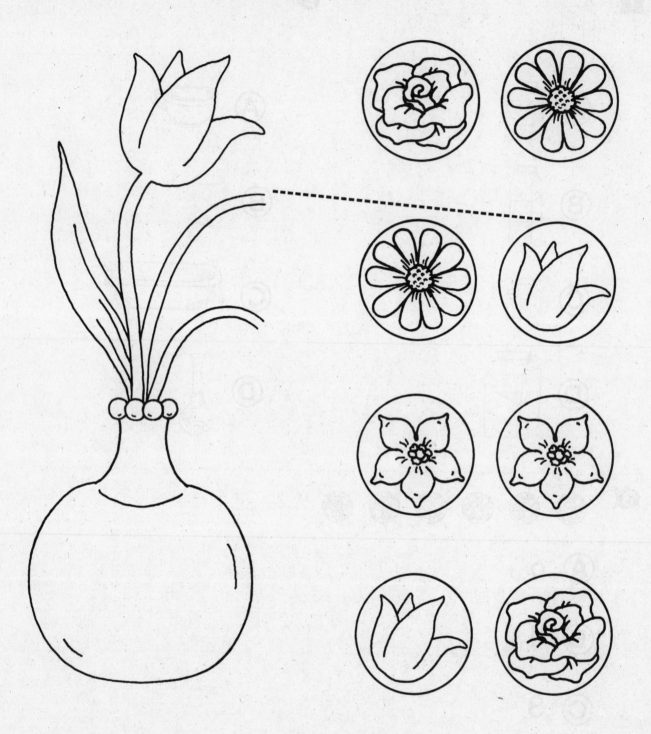

---

**Directions** Have children find the flower stickers that are the same as the flower in the vase and draw a line from them to the stems in the vase.

# Same and Different

  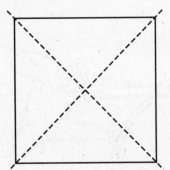 

 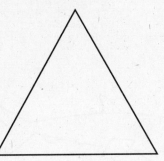 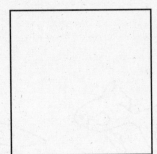 

 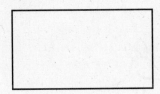 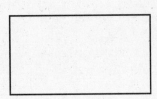 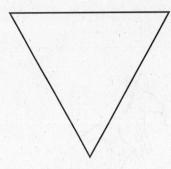

 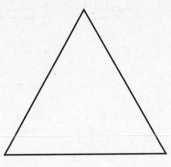  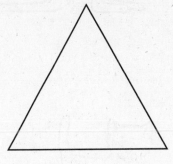

**Directions** Have children color the same two items in each row the same color. Have them mark an X on the item in each row that is different from the other two items.

**P 13·1**

Name _____

# Look-Alikes

 **1**

**2**

**3**

**4**

**Directions** Have children mark an X on the item in each row that is different from the other two items.

E 13·1

Name _____

 **1**

Ⓐ

Ⓑ

Ⓒ

Ⓓ

 **2**

Ⓐ

Ⓑ

Ⓒ

Ⓓ

**3**

**Directions** Have children: **1** fill in the bubble next to the picture that shows the object that is different from the other 3 items; **2** fill in the bubble next to the picture that shows the object that is different from the others; **3** circle the object that is different from the others.

Name _____

# Sorting by One Attribute

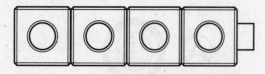

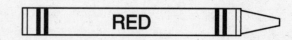

RED

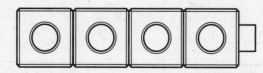

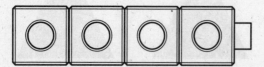

2

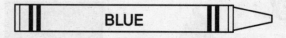

BLUE

**Directions** Display a container with 8 red and 8 blue cubes. Have children: ★ take a handful of cubes, sort the red cubes by placing 1 on each cube outline, then color the outlines to show their red cubes; ② take another handful, sort the blue cubes, then color to show their blue cubes.

**R 13·2**

# Sorting by One Attribute

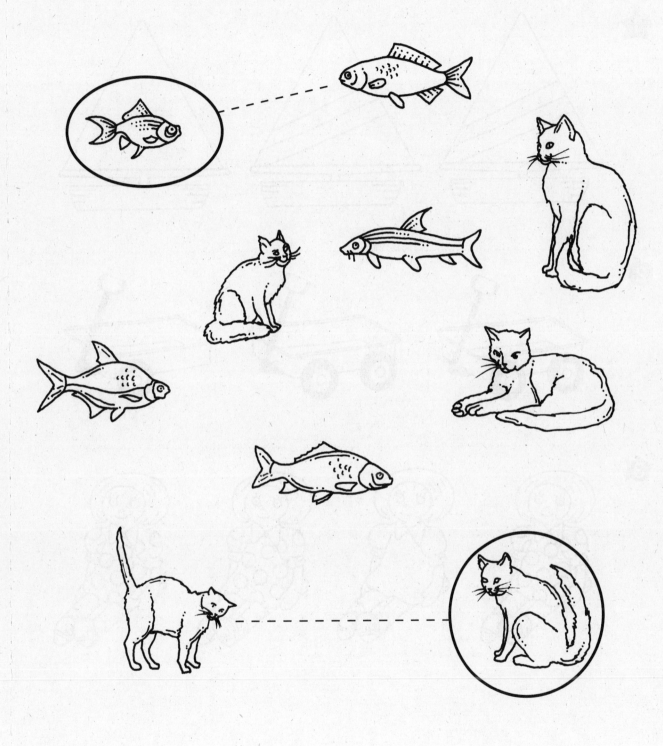

**Directions** Have children sort the cats and the fish by drawing lines to the appropriate circles.

P 13·2

# Toyland

**1**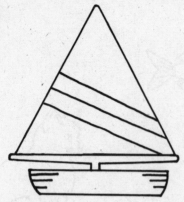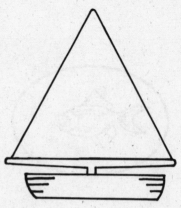

**2**

**3**

---

**Directions** Have children find the toy that is different in each group. Then have them draw the missing part.

⭐ 1

Ⓐ Ⓑ Ⓒ Ⓓ

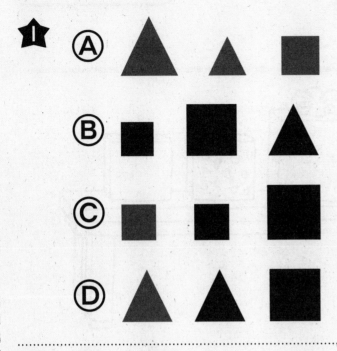

🍎 2

Ⓐ Ⓑ Ⓒ Ⓓ

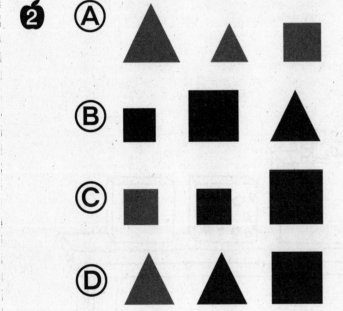

③

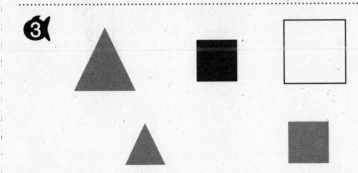

**Directions** Have children: ⭐ fill in the bubble next to the picture that shows the shapes sorted by size; 🍎 fill in the bubble next to the picture that shows the shapes sorted by shape; ③ circle the shapes to sort them by color.

Name _____

# Sorting the Same Set
# in Different Ways

**1**

**2**

---

**Directions** Have children: **1** sort the presents one way and circle the presents to show how they sorted; **2** sort the same presents a different way and circle to show how they sorted.

# Sorting the Same Set in Different Ways

**Directions** Have children: ★ sort the balloons by circling all the large balloons; ② sort the balloons by circling all the shaded balloons.

Name _____

# Join the Club!

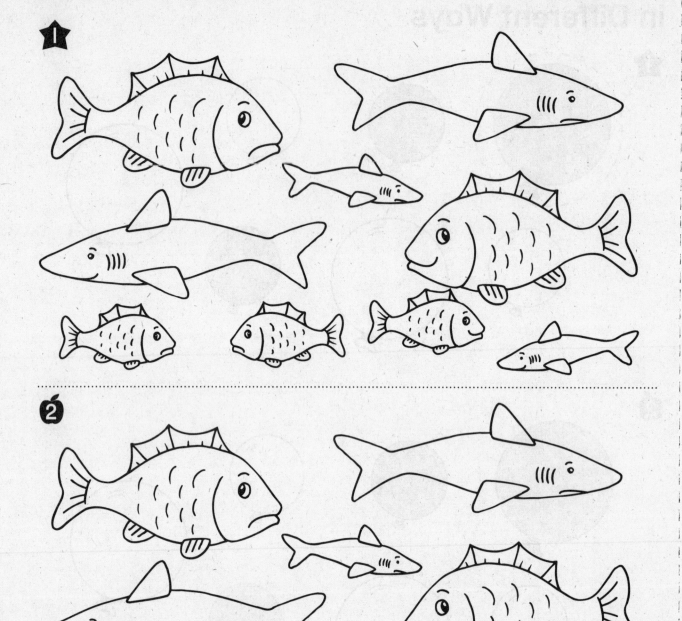

**Directions** Have children: ❶ sort the fish by coloring the large fish red; ❷ sort the fish in a different way by coloring the group blue.

E 13-3

Copyright © Pearson Education, Inc., or its affiliates. All Rights Reserved. **K**

Name _____

 **1**

 A

 B

 C

 D

 **2**

 A

 B

 C

 D

**3**

**Directions** Have children: **1** fill in the bubble next to the picture that shows objects that are the same shape and same color; **2** fill in the bubble next to the picture that shows the objects that are the same color and same kind; **3** draw 2 balls that are different from each other.

**D 13·4**

Name _____

# Sorting by More
# Than One Attribute

 1

2

**Directions** Have children: ⭐ sort the shapes one way by drawing them in the space provided; ② sort the shapes a different way by drawing them. Then ask children to explain how they sorted each set, by shape, design, or size.

Name _____

# Sorting By More Than One Attribute

**1**

**2**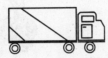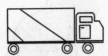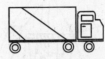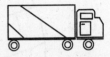

**3**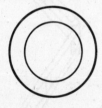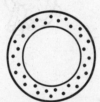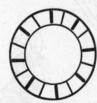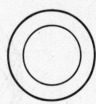

**4**

**Directions** Have children look at the objects in each row and mark an X on the object that doesn't belong.

Name _____

# Take Me Home

**Directions** Have children circle the gray standing animals. Then have them sort the animals in a different way by drawing an X over animals with a different pair of attributes in common (e.g., white horses, sitting sheep).

Name _____

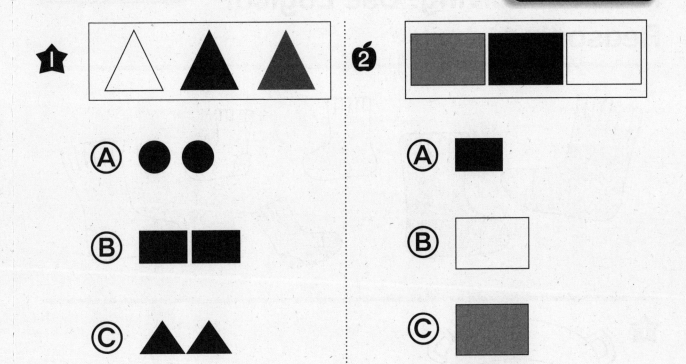

⭐1

Ⓐ ● ●

Ⓑ ■■

Ⓒ ▲▲

Ⓓ ■ ■

🍎2

Ⓐ ▪

Ⓑ ▫

Ⓒ ▪

Ⓓ ▪

③

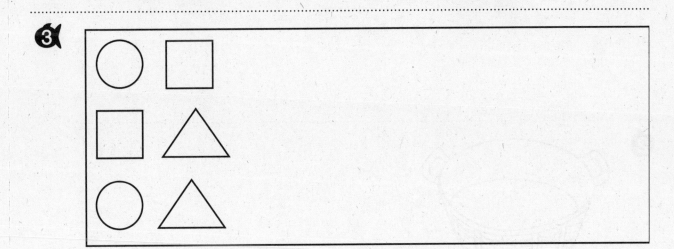

**Directions** Have children: ⭐ fill in the bubble next to the picture that shows how the blocks are sorted; 🍎 fill in the bubble next to the picture of a block that does not belong with the sorted blocks; ③ draw 2 more shapes that belong in the group.

# Problem Solving: Use Logical Reasoning

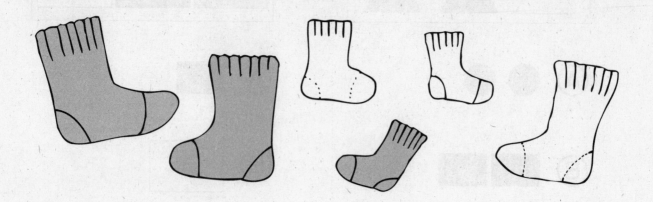

**❶**

**❷**

**Directions** Have children: ❶ use yellow and red crayons to draw the socks and sort them by color; ❷ draw socks to sort them by size.

Name _____

# Problem Solving: Use Logical Reasoning

**1**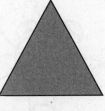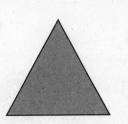

**2**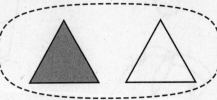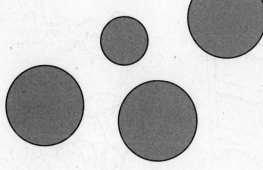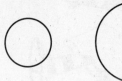

**3**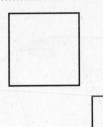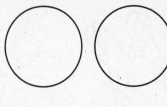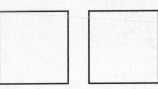

**Directions** For each exercise, have children identify how the attribute blocks are sorted on the left and circle the blocks on the right that show the sorting rule.

Name _____

# What Goes Where?

**Directions** Have children look at each type of chest and then draw lines from each item to the correct chest.

Ⓐ

Ⓒ

Ⓑ

Ⓓ

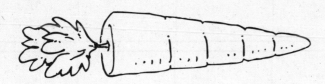

Ⓐ  2 + 3 = 5

Ⓑ  2 + 5 = 7

Ⓒ  5 + 3 = 8

Ⓓ  4 + 4 = 8

**Directions** Have children: ❶ fill in the bubble next to the picture that shows the object that is lighter than the sneaker shown; ❷ fill in the bubble next to the number sentence that tells the story in the picture; ❸ draw a longer carrot below the one shown.

Name _____

# Real Graphs

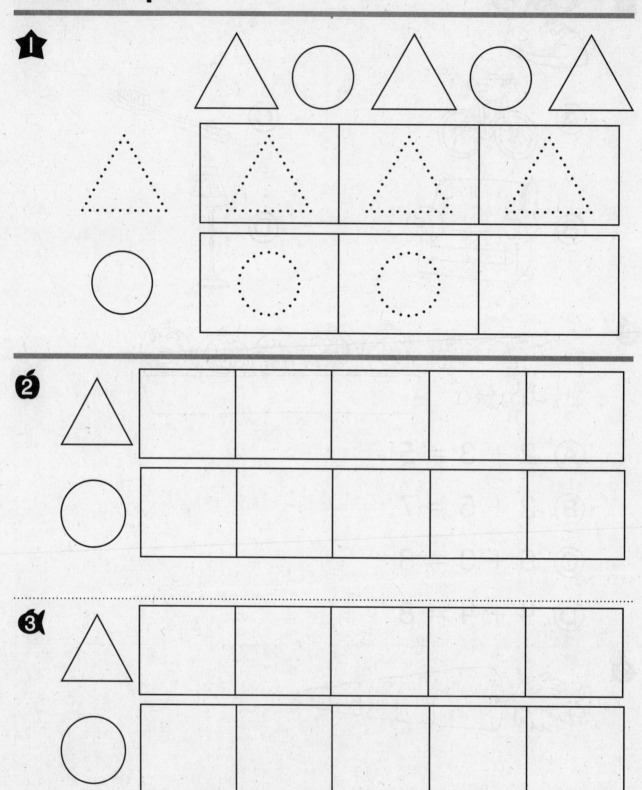

---

**Directions** Children will need the attribute blocks shown for these exercises. Have children: ⭐ sort the blocks by shape, trace each shape, and circle the row with the most shapes; ❷—❸ take a handful of triangle and circle blocks, sort them by shape, and draw how many of each type they pick up each time in the graphs.

Name _____

# Real Graphs

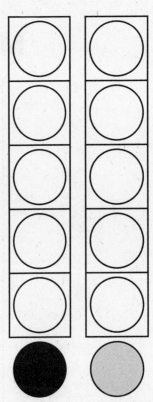

---

---

**Directions** Have children: ★—② color to show the number of each color counter in the graphs on the right and circle the column that shows which group has fewer objects.

# Counter Drop

## More Red or More Yellow?

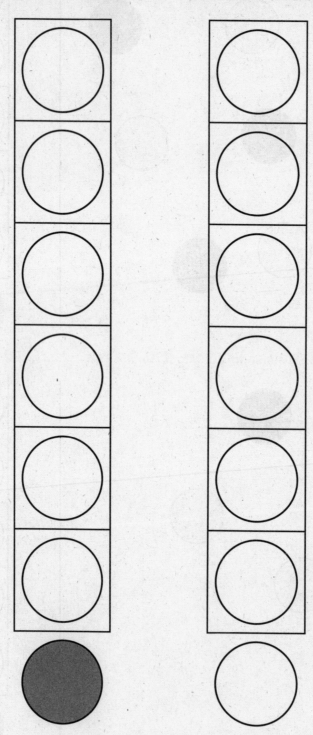

**Directions** Have children toss a 2-color counter and color one counter on the graph red or yellow to show how it landed. Repeat tossing the counter and coloring the graph until one column is full. Have children tell the results as more red or more yellow.

Name _____

**1**

Ⓐ

Ⓑ

Ⓒ

Ⓓ

**2**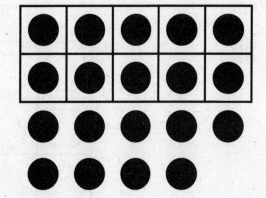

Ⓐ 16

Ⓑ 17

Ⓒ 18

Ⓓ 19

**3**

---

**Directions** Have children: **1** fill in the bubble next to the picture that shows the object that is the same as the others; **2** fill in the bubble next to the number that tells how many counters; **3** color the rabbit that is second in line from the carrots.

# Picture Graphs

**1**

**2**

**3**

**4**

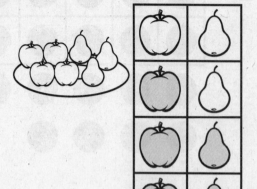

---

**Directions** Have children look at the fruit on each plate and color a picture on the graph for each one. Then have children circle the fruit at the bottom of the column that shows more.

# Picture Graphs

**1**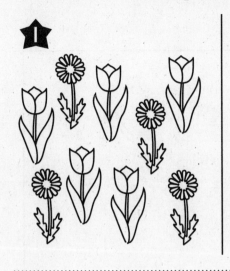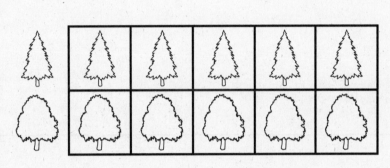

**2**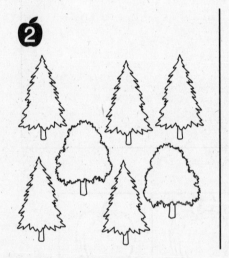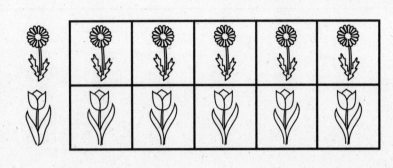

**3**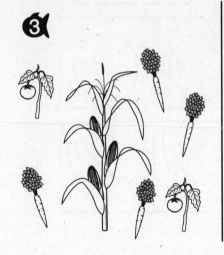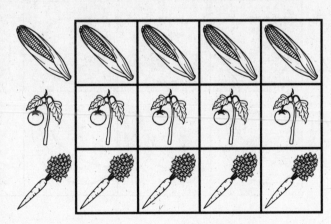

**Directions** Have children look at the objects in each picture and color a picture on the graph for each object. Then have them circle the row in each graph that has the most objects.

# Picture a Graph

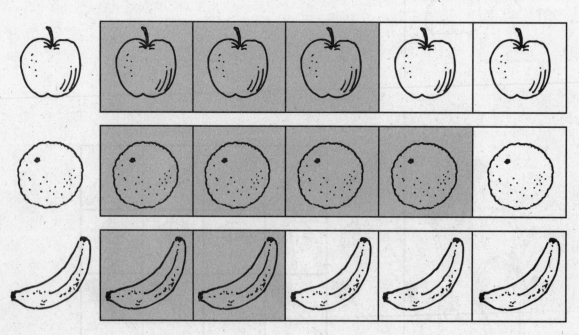

**Directions** Have children draw a picture using the same number of apples, oranges, and bananas as pictured on the graph. Ask them to tell what the picture shows.